PROBOSCIS MONKEYS
OF BORNEO

D0398150

PROBOSCIS MONKEYS
OF BORNEO

Second Edition

Elizabeth L. Bennett

Natural History Publications (Borneo)
Kota Kinabalu

2013

Published by

Natural History Publications (Borneo) Sdn. Bhd. (216807-X)
A913, 9th Floor, Wisma Merdeka Phase 1
P.O. Box 15566
88864 Kota Kinabalu, Sabah, Malaysia
Tel: 088-233098 Fax: 088-240768
e-mail: info@nhpborneo.com
website: www.nhpborneo.com

Copyright © 1993, 2013 Natural History Publications (Borneo) Sdn. Bhd.

All rights reserved. No part of this publication may be reproduced, stored in a
retrieval system, or transmitted in any form or by any means, electronic, mechanical,
photo-copying, recording, or otherwise, without the prior permission of the copyright
owners.

First published 1993
Second Edition published January 2013

Proboscis Monkeys of Borneo
Second Edition
    by Elizabeth L. Bennett

ISBN 978-983-812-139-2

Front cover: Warning off an approaching rival male with a honk and display of
teeth! Photo: J. & C. Sohns/PhotoAsia, Malaysia.
Back cover: Sunrise at Sukau, part of the amazing natural wonder of the area.
Photo: Arthur Chung.
Endpapers: A riverine forest at the Kinabatangan River. Photo: Rudi Delvaux.
Half-title page: A large male proboscis monkey with its pendulous nose.
Photo: W. Layer/PhotoAsia, Malaysia.
Frontispiece: A male proboscis monkey. Painting by Phillip Yong.

Printed in Taiwan.

Contents

Photo: Rudi Delvaux.

First Impressions

When anybody sees a proboscis monkey in the wild for the first time, they are staggered. Not uncommonly, they make a remark such as "I don't believe that animal!". Even seeing them in zoos is not enough to be prepared for seeing these extraordinary animals in their natural habitat, with all the noise and spectacle involved.

Proboscis monkeys have been making spectacular first impressions on people for a long time. Early naturalists could not agree, though, whether the animals were amazingly wonderful or amazingly grotesque. One of the earliest reports of proboscis monkeys in the wild came from British officer Hugh Low. As long ago as 1848, he said that the proboscis monkey "is remarkable for its very long nose; it is a very fine monkey, in size approaching the orang-utan, but much less disgusting in appearance". Another early explorer-naturalist, Odoardo Beccari, obviously had somewhat mixed feelings about the animals. On the one hand, he said that "the long-nosed ape is of singular and ridiculous aspect", but went on "Why amongst all apes...this one should be provided with a long, prominent and fleshy nose, somewhat hooked at its extremity, it is hard to say. According to Darwinian theory, it might possibly be attributed to sexual selection. If such were the case, we might, perhaps, congratulate the monkey on its good taste".

The calls of the proboscis monkey were also a subject of praise. In 1928, the then curator of the Sarawak Museum, Eric Mjoberg, wrote that "the enormous nose is a sounding board that strengthens and deepens the male's vocal powers....The sound is deep and nasal, strongly reminiscent of the bass viol. Possibly, too, there is some aesthetic touch in it, for the females find the sound attractive and crowd round their musically gifted leader".

Fig. 1 (opposite). Reproduced from D.G. Elliott *A Review of the Primates, Volume III. Anthropoidea: Miopithecus to Pan*. American Museum of Natural History, New York (1912). **Fig. 2** (above). Reproduced from E. Mjoberg's *Forest Life and Adventures in the Malay Archipelago*. George Allen and Unwin, London (1930).

These early observers were not always so enthusiastic. Low went on to say of the proboscis monkey: "his appearance is highly ludicrous, he rejoices in a pendulous fleshy nose which droops at the end almost over his mouth. This appendage has no apparent use, and is not even decorative". After he had complimented the monkey's calls, Mjoberg wrote that its nose "puts even the most exaggerated and splendid Bourbon nose into the shade. It is a bright red, fleshy appendage....that projects far above the mouth and partly blocks its entrance. When the owner in question has to satisfy his stomach's insistent demands, his pushes his 'stop-cock' to one side with his hand, a most comical proceeding".

One of Mjoberg's successors as Curator of the Sarawak Museum, the well-known Tom Harrisson, referred in 1938 to "the vile porty-looking proboscis monkey", and as late as 1965, a paper was written by the American J.A. Kern entitled "Grotesque honker of the Bornean swamps".

So what is the animal that produces such strong but conflicting reactions really like? And what is it about the animal that causes such comment? This short book introduces you to proboscis monkeys by telling you about them and their behaviour. It also includes discussion about the problems facing them, their conservation and future prospects. It concludes with a short guide to where you can easily see them and how to get there.

Fig. 3 (above). A 4-cent stamp issued by the then British North Borneo in 1939 was the first postage stamp ever published of this odd primate.
Fig. 4. Proboscis monkeys sometimes travel on the ground between trees, especially in mangrove areas at low tide. Photo: Ch'ien C. Lee.

What are Proboscis Monkeys?

Proboscis monkeys belong to the group of mammals called Primates. Unlike many other groups of mammals, you cannot point to one particular feature of a primate and say right, that is what makes this animal a primate. Instead, primates are characterised by having most or all of a range of features. Most or all primates have hands and feet well adapted for grasping objects, with separated and very mobile fingers and toes, and nails rather than claws. They also have their eyes at the front of their heads, not round the sides, so have good stereoscopic sight like humans. And they generally have relatively larger brains than other animals.

The order Primates includes humans, as well as apes (chimpanzees and gorillas of Africa, and orang-utans and gibbons of Asia), all the monkeys, and a group of smaller, generally nocturnal animals known as prosimians. Monkeys of the Old World (Africa and Eurasia) and New World (America) are very different and not especially closely related. Only New World monkeys have prehensile or clinging tails, for example.

In the Old World, monkeys fall clearly into two groups known as cercopithecines and colobines. Proboscis monkeys are colobines. They say that the way to a man's heart is through his stomach, so with a colobine, it is a hard task indeed since colobines have the most enormous stomachs. It is these which distinguish colobines from cercopithecine monkeys such as macaques and baboons. A colobine's stomach is divided into several sections, similar to that of a cow. Like a cow's, a colobine's stomach is full of a

Fig. 5. With their often human-like expressions and upright posture, adult male proboscis monkeys have been making spectacular first impressions on people for a long time. Photo: Ch'ien C. Lee.

Fig. 6. Infant proboscis monkeys travel by clinging to their mother's front. Photo: K. Wothe/PhotoAsia, Malaysia.

soup containing huge numbers of bacteria which ferment the animal's food. This allows it to digest leaves to obtain energy; animals with normal, simple stomachs, including humans, cannot do this.

The ability to obtain energy by eating leaves means that, in terms of numbers, colobines are by far the most successful primates in the tropical rain forests of Africa and Asia; in any one forest, about two-thirds of the primates are colobines. In African forests, these are colobus monkeys, and in Asia, they are the langurs or leaf monkeys of South and South-east Asia, such as the banded, silvered and red langurs, as well as the beautiful and exotic looking douc and golden monkeys of Indochina and China. The latter two species groups, together with the simakobu of the Mentawai Islands near Sumatra, all have rather unusual noses and, with the proboscis monkey, are known as "odd-nosed colobines". None of the others has a nose in the same outsize class as the proboscis monkey, but they are all unusual and upturned, and their odd noses and various other features similar to the proboscis monkey mean that these are the proboscis monkeys' closest relatives.

The colobines' specialised stomachs allow them to thrive in forests, but mean that they do not do so well in more open environments, including those heavily influenced by humans. The colobine's digestive system that adapts them so well to eating leaves actually precludes them from eating many other foods: sugary fruits are broken down so rapidly by the bacteria in the stomach that the result is a rapid build-up of acid and gas, causing the monkeys to become sick or even die of an appalling-sounding condition known as bloat. So outside the leafy forest, the more versatile cercopithecines come into their own. With stomachs more similar to ours, they can eat a wide variety of items in the more open areas, including fruits, birds' eggs and crabs, and sometimes even human crops. So it is the cercopithecines with which we are generally more familiar. That is not because they are more common overall; it is that they tend to thrive in areas where humans live. In the forests, colobines predominate.

Proboscis monkeys are particularly extreme, even for colobines. Their stomachs are relatively twice as large as those of any of their relatives. This means that, to the uninitiated, proboscis monkeys appear permanently pregnant — even the males! Their enormous, bloated stomachs and huge, pendulous noses have given rise to one of their less flattering names, *orang belanda* or 'Dutchman', since the animals reminded people in Borneo of Europeans.

Figs. 7 (left) & **8** (right). Infant proboscis monkeys are dependent on their mothers for up to two years, as they mature from being dark furred and blue-faced, to the brown colour of adulthood. Photos: FLPA/Jurgen & Christi (left) and J. & C. Sohns (right)/ PhotoAsia, Malaysia.

Orang belanda is still the name most commonly used for the animals in Sarawak, especially in the west. In other parts of Borneo, a wide range of names is used for the monkeys, including *rasong*, *raseng*, *pika*, *bekantan*, *bentangan* and *bangketan*.

It is the adult male proboscis monkey which is so extreme and striking. Weighing an average of 20 kg, he is very large for a tree-dwelling animal, and indeed, he is one of the largest monkeys in the world. He has a pink-brown coloured face, and his huge, pendulous and greatly expanded fleshy nose does indeed overhang his mouth, forcing him to push it up out of the way when he eats. Proboscis monkeys are mainly reddish-brown, with grey lower limbs. The male has a darker cap over the top of his head, a yellow collar and a thick, dark brown mane of fur on his back which resembles an old bomber jacket acquired in his youth and into which he is now trying to cram his middle-aged spread. At the back below his short jacket, he has a strikingly white rump patch of much shorter fur, leading into a thick white tail.

Although she shares most of the same basic features as the male, a female proboscis monkey is altogether a more modest looking animal. She is only about half his weight, around 10 kg. Like the male, she is also mainly red-brown with a flesh-coloured face, but she does not have his striking contrasts of colour. Moreover, her nose is not huge and pendulous. In younger females, it is fairly short and snubby, and even noses of older females which droop somewhat never reach the enormous dimensions of the male's and never reach as low as the mouth. This means that it is easy to pick out a male from any angle. Even if the only thing visible through the leaves is a row of tails, the male is the one whose tail is thickest and whitest.

New-born proboscis monkeys look quite different from the adults, but are also striking. They are covered with sparse, blackish fur and have blue faces with snubby, upturned noses. Their fur turns brown quite quickly, and by the time the monkey is about four months old, it is roughly the same colour as an adult's. The face slowly turns greyish, but does not lose its bluish tinge totally until it is about a year old.

Not only are proboscis monkeys unusual to look at; they also make the most bizarre range of noises. Roars, grunts, squeals and a huge range of nasal honks mean that, from a distance, a group of proboscis monkeys through the trees can sound somewhat akin to a group of grumbling old men. And the occasional roars from a male sound like a far larger and more dangerous animal than a monkey! Most commonly, different proboscis monkeys in a group start to honk and squeal, then the male gives a gentle and deep nasal "ho-hooong", which seems to calm them down and peace is restored.

Where are Proboscis Monkeys Found?

The only place in the world where proboscis monkeys occur is the island of Borneo in South-east Asia. And they are not even found throughout all of Borneo. They are forest-dwellers and are limited mainly to coastal swamp forests and to forests next to large rivers, mainly in the coastal plains although they do occur further inland immediately adjacent to large rivers in Kalimantan and in the inland swamps of Danau Sentarum and Mahakam Lakes. The species is never found above 350 metres above sea level. Even more limiting, they are not found in all areas of riverine and coastal swamp forests. Many riverine forests are devoid of proboscis monkeys, even in the coastal plains. Coastal swamp forests mainly comprise mangrove and peat swamp. Both of these habitats have different zones, where different types of trees occur somewhat patchily, depending on distance from the coast or

Fig. 9. The river snakes its way across the flat land, overflowing its banks each rainy season to create a floodplain. Photo: C.L. Chan.

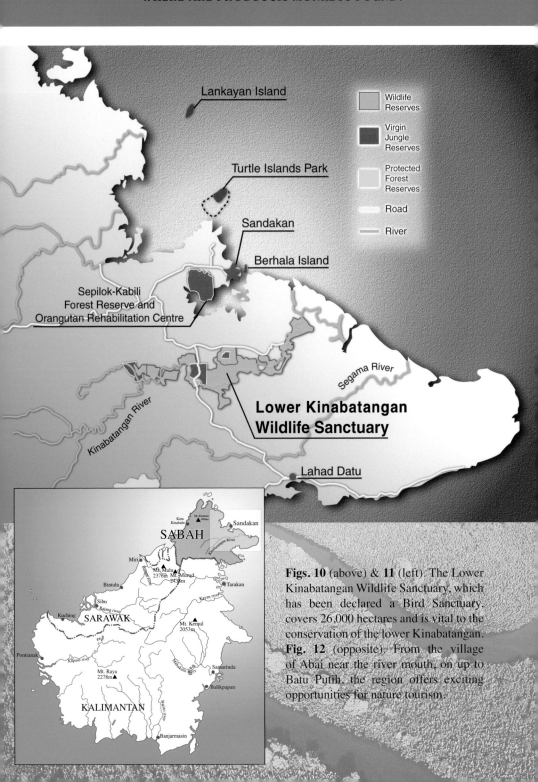

Lankayan Island

Turtle Islands Park

Sandakan

Berhala Island

Sepilok-Kabili
Forest Reserve and
Orangutan Rehabilitation Centre

Segama River

**Lower Kinabatangan
Wildlife Sanctuary**

Kinabatangan River

Lahad Datu

Wildlife
Reserves

Virgin
Jungle
Reserves

Protected
Forest
Reserves

Road

River

Kota
Kinabalu
Mt. Kinabalu
4094m

Sandakan

SABAH

Miri

Kinabatangan River

Mt. Mulu
2376m
Mt. Murud
2433m

Tarakan

Bintulu

Kayan river

Sibu

Rajang river

Kuching

SARAWAK

Mt. Kemul
2053m

Pontianak

Kapuas river

Mahakam river

Samarinda

Mt. Raya
2278m

Balikpapan

KALIMANTAN

Barito river

Banjarmasin

Figs. 10 (above) & **11** (left). The Lower Kinabatangan Wildlife Sanctuary, which has been declared a Bird Sanctuary, covers 26,000 hectares and is vital to the conservation of the lower Kinabatangan. **Fig. 12** (opposite). From the village of Abai near the river mouth, on up to Batu Putih, the region offers exciting opportunities for nature tourism.

centre of the peat swamp. Proboscis monkeys are found in most of these forest zones, but not all. For example, it is uncommon to find them in large patches of nipa mangrove; extensive stands of the brackish-water nipa palm form an inhospitable area with little food for a monkey. On the other hand, in some areas of riverine and peat swamp forests, they reach very high densities. Again, this is partly due to differences in vegetation, but also possibly to historical patterns of shifting landforms and human disturbance. So it is misleading to assume that any area of riverine, mangrove or peat swamp forest is full of proboscis monkeys. Only by going there to look can you be sure.

Although proboscis monkeys are mainly restricted to coastal areas, small numbers are occasionally found much further inland next to major rivers including the Segama and the Kinabatangan in Sabah and Barito in

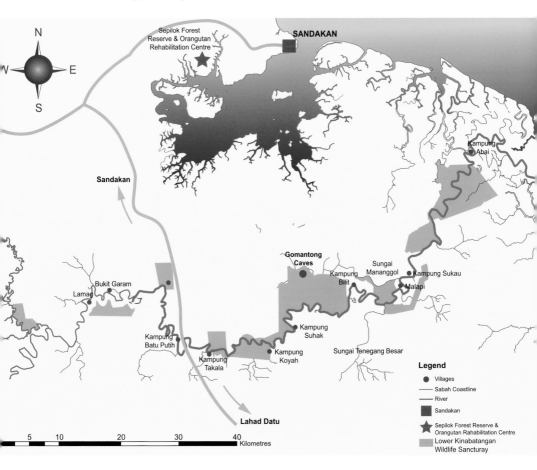

Fig. 13. Travelling along Bornean rivers in the late afternoon, with possibilities of seeing proboscis monkeys and a wide variety of other spectacular animals, is an unforgettable experience. Photo: Rudi Delvaux.

Kalimantan. There are even scanty reports of animals passing briefly through hill forests far in the interior. This is extremely rare, and such animals are probably on their own and nomadic.

Nobody knows why proboscis monkeys have such a very limited distribution, and why they are not found in the vast tracts of rain forest throughout inland Borneo. On higher ground, it is possibly related to the lack of minerals or other nutrients. Inland forests of Borneo grow on notoriously

Fig. 14. The junction of the Menanggol River, a prime area for spotting proboscis monkeys. Photo: C.L. Chan.

poor soils. Proboscis monkeys are large animals so they need an ample supply of digestible food. This is most likely to be found where forests grow on nutrient-rich alluvial soils such as mangroves or alongside rivers. Increasingly, researchers are thinking that one reason why proboscis monkeys are not more common along Borneo's major rivers is past hunting, although further research is needed to determine if this is true. If it is, then it gives hope that, if hunting is controlled, proboscis monkeys might be able to expand their range again in the future.

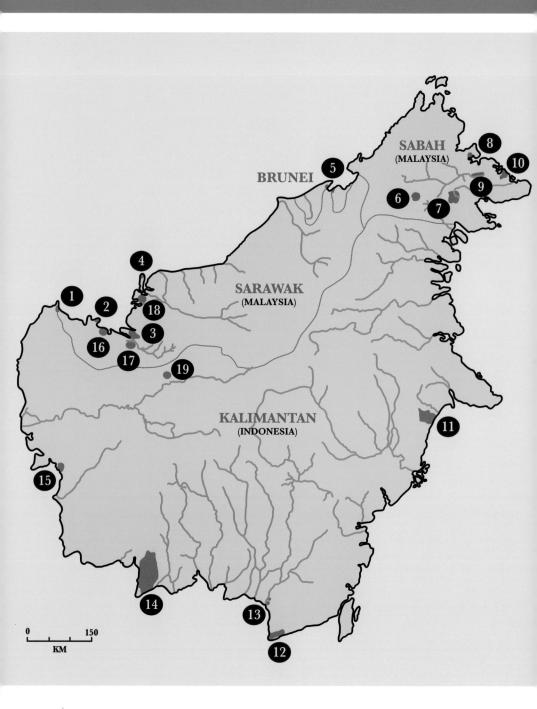

Bornean Reserves where Proboscis Monkeys are Found

Being restricted mainly to coastal areas, proboscis monkeys are not found in many of the large, inland reserves of Borneo. Pressure on land in coastal and riverine areas in Borneo is intense, so most coastal reserves are small, and the monkeys often use areas inside and outside the reserves. Reserves which are too small to protect a viable population of proboscis monkeys if all the forest surrounding them were to be cleared, or which are marginal habitat with low numbers of the monkeys, are marked with a *.

Throughout the entire range of the proboscis monkey, then, the only reserves known definitely to be large enough to sustain a population if isolated are Lower Kinabatangan Wildlife Sanctuary in Sabah, possibly Maludam National Park in Sarawak and, in Kalimantan, Danau Sentarum Wildlife Reserve, Tanjung Puting National Park and possibly Gunung Palung National Park.

Fig. 15 (opposite): Map of Borneo.
1. Samunsam Wildlife Sanctuary *
2. Bako National Park *
3. Maludam National Park
4. Bruit-Patok National Park *
5. Pulau Siarau and Pulau Beramban Primary Conservation Areas *
6. Maliau Basin Conservation Area *
7. Danum Valley Conservation Area *
8. Sepilok Forest Reserve *
9. Lower Kinabatangan Wildlife Sanctuary
10. Kulamba Wildlife Reserve *
11. Kutai National Park *
12. Pleihari Tana Laut Wildlife Reserve *
13. Pulau Kembang and Pulau Kaget Wildlife Reserve *
14. Tanjung Puting National Park
15. Gunung Palung National Park *
16. Kuching Wetland National Park *
17. Sedilu National Park *
18. Rajang Mangrove National Park *
19. Danau Sentarum National Park

Fig. 16. Dawn in the flooded riverine forests of Borneo. Photo: Paul Swen.

Distribution of
Proboscis Monkeys

T he only recent wide-scale surveys of proboscis monkeys have been conducted in Sabah; all others were more than ten years ago, and with rapid recent changes across Borneo, the map is inevitably an approximation. It is based on records from the most recent surveys in each area and the location of potentially suitable habitat.

Fig. 17. Map of Borneo showing coastal distribution of proboscis monkeys.

Fig. 18. When a proboscis monkey harem is in an open tree beside the river, it is easy to count and identify them. Photo: Rudi Delvaux.

The Social Life of Proboscis Monkeys

When you first look at proboscis monkeys in the wild, it seems that their social life is chaotic. Sometimes there are just one or two animals, sometimes about ten, and sometimes huge, noisy hordes of 80 or more. Early observers could not agree on what was happening, whether the animals lived in small groups with only one male, or if they were in much larger ones, with many males and females. The impression was that there was no set social system, merely random associations of monkeys. That would be highly unusual. No animals live in a state of social chaos, especially not higher primates which have strict patterns and rules governing their social lives.

In fact, proboscis monkeys do have a set social system, but it is more flexible, and possibly more subtle, than that of many other primates. They live in harems which are groups containing one male, one to about ten females and their offspring. The size of harems varies, possibly differing between habitats

Fig. 19. Adult male proboscis monkey, with four of his females close behind. It is unusual for the male to lead the group. Photo: Arthur Chung.

Fig. 20. The closest bonds in proboscis monkey society are between females and their young offspring. Photo: FLPA/Jurgen & Christi/PhotoAsia, Malaysia.

with somewhat larger groups in riverine forests than in mangroves, but the normal range is between nine and about 18 animals.

Living in harems is not unusual — most primates and many other mammals have social systems based in some way round a harem. What is unusual about proboscis monkeys is that the harems do not stay apart and avoid others. It seems that the social system has two tiers: the smaller, relatively stable harem, and a larger band of several harems which live in the same area and which frequently meet and aggregate together, especially by riversides in the evening. This explains the large hordes of animals sometimes spotted.

The other unusual thing about proboscis monkeys is the frequency with which animals move between different social groups. Usually, animals stay in the social group they know. If one sex moves between groups to avoid inbreeding, the other stays behind with its relatives. However, both male and female proboscis monkeys sometimes move between social groups. Females switch between harems at any time from before adolescence onwards, and they might change groups several times in their lives. Males are kicked out of

Figs. 21 (left) & **22** (right). If adult males are to keep their harem, they have to show off to attract females — and display to deter rival males. Photos: FLPA/Jurgen & Christi (left) and Ernest Manewal (right)/PhotoAsia, Malaysia.

Fig. 23. Warning off an approaching rival male with a honk and display of teeth!
Photo: J. & C. Sohns/PhotoAsia, Malaysia.

Fig. 24 (above). About 18 months old, this young proboscis monkey is highly agile and travelling independently — although might still cling to its mother to sleep at night. Photo: Rudi Delvaux. **Fig. 25** (below). Partially-webbed back feet allow this young male proboscis monkey to travel easily on mangrove mud without sinking in. Photo: Ch'ien C. Lee. **Fig. 26** (opposite). Their outsized stomachs mean that proboscis monkeys look permanently pregnant — even if they are obviously male! Photo: Paul Swen.

Fig. 27. It is often difficult to distinguish all-male groups from harems. Photo: Rudi Delvaux.

the group in which they were born when they are only just old enough to fend for themselves, maybe when they are only one to two years old. They team up with other males to form all-male groups. These typically comprise one or two large males and ten or more small ones. This is misleading for the unwary observer because they look very like harems, with one large animal and many smaller ones. The illusion of a harem is further enhanced by young males clinging to older ones to sleep at night, in much the same way as they would have clung to their mothers. All-male groups also congregate with harems along the riverbanks, and often follow harems during the day as they travel through the forest.

For a male proboscis monkey, coming close to other harems and, even worse, being followed by all-male groups means that other males are sometimes close to his females. This is a major problem. Either the females might be enticed away, or another male might sneak in for a quick mating while his back is turned. So, if another group is nearby, a harem male often gives a highly spectacular display of strength. He is trying to show his, and possibly other, females how big, strong and handsome he is. At the same time, he is telling other males that he is a formidable opponent so stay away from his females!

Fig. 28. Members of a group feeding quietly together in a tree. Photo: Joseph Tangah.

The first stage of a display involves a male staring hard at his opponent, leaning forward on all fours with his chin thrust forwards or his mouth wide open. If that does not have the desired effect, the male then suddenly and unpredictably leaps through the trees, often with a loud roar, and frequently landing on dead branches which break with a sharp crack, adding to the general uproar. It is rare for confrontations between males to escalate to actual physical contact. Chases between males are not infrequent though, and sometimes one male will chase another so suddenly that the latter leaps off his branch and lands with a loud splash in the river below. If the males do actually make contact, they have slapping contests. Judging from occasional scars, it seems that males sometimes get injured in fights, but it is probably quite rare. Showing their strength using displays means that males can assess their chances of winning a battle, so do not attempt one if their chances of success are low or if sustaining injury seems likely.

Once harmony with other groups has been restored, proboscis monkeys can resume their social life inside their own group. Compared to some monkeys such as macaques, social life within the group is fairly quiet. Most interactions between animals are infants and juveniles playing with each other, having chasing, grappling and swinging games through the branches. Adult females

Fig. 29 (above). Adult male proboscis monkeys sometimes have to push their noses up out of the way when they eat. Photo: Berndt Fischer/PhotoAsia, Malaysia. **Fig. 30** (below left). Juvenile proboscis monkeys playing at Labuk Bay, Sabah. **Fig. 31** (below right). Macaques and proboscis monkeys eat different types of foods, so are not competing and can feed peacefully together. Photos: Joseph Tangah.

Opposite: Fig. 32 (above). All-male groups of proboscis monkeys are quite common. Photo: Rudi Delvaux. **Fig. 33** (below left). Juvenile proboscis monkeys are agile climbers. Photo: J. & C. Sohns/PhotoAsia, Malaysia. **Fig. 34** (below right). But even when growing up, they still spend much time sitting with their mothers. Photo: Juan Carlos Muñoz/PhotoAsia, Malaysia.

spend some time grooming their infants but, unlike many other primates, grooming between adults is rare. The only physical interaction often seen between the adult male and his females is mating, and even that is inclined to be seasonal, with a peak around the middle of the year. This corresponds with a peak in births around the turn of the year. Although much smaller than the male, a female proboscis monkey is apparently not shy of him and sometimes initiates the mating. She does this by presenting her back to the male, leaning forward on all fours, and turning her head over her shoulder to face him, waggling her head from side to side and pouting her lips.

Fig. 35. Female proboscis monkeys might move between different harems several times in their lives. Photo: Marc Ancrenaz.

Even when he has secured his females from other males and one is presenting herself before him, a harem male faces problems. When mating starts, the young animals in the group become extremely upset and do everything they can to interfere. They frequently pull hard on the male's upper leg, screaming all the while, but a more successful tactic is to lean over the amorous couple from the front and try to tweak the male's nose. Even if this does not stop mating immediately, it certainly curtails a male's ardour. He sometimes even has to stop what he is doing to chase away the youngsters before returning to his female. The ultimate frustration must be when he finds that, in the meantime, the female has lost interest and wandered away.

Big Noses

T he most common question that people ask about proboscis monkeys is: Why does the male have such a huge nose? Answers to this over the years have been many and varied. Proboscis monkeys are proficient swimmers, so it was suggested that the nose acts as a snorkel to help the animals breathe when swimming. This fails to explain why females, in that case, do not drown. Another theory was that the nose is mainly a function of body size: the larger the male, the larger the nose. This does not explain why the nose grows relatively faster than the rest of the body, and is also negated by the fact that when a young male proboscis monkey grows, his body is full sized before his nose expands fully.

Another common misconception is that the nose "balloons" up when the monkey calls, amplifying resonant alarm honks. The nose does move forward slightly when a male calls, but that is purely a function of its being in front of the mouth and the male pushing his chin up when calling. The nose does not increase in size.

The reason why both sexes have larger noses than other primates might have something to do with regulating body temperature. Coastal swamp forests especially are hot and humid, and proboscis monkeys are larger than any other monkeys living there so have a greater problem of heat loss. They also have large, fermenting-chamber stomachs inside them which must generate a lot of heat. So they could well suffer from overheating. A big nose provides a large surface area from which to lose heat, in much the same way as the ears of an elephant do. This

Fig. 36. To female proboscis monkeys, long noses are the ultimate in good looks. Photo: FLPA/Jurgen & Christi/ PhotoAsia, Malaysia.

could explain why proboscis monkeys have big noses in the first place, but not why the male's carries on growing after he has reached his full body size.

The most likely explanation for the male's nose was hit upon by Beccari as long ago as 1904, when he attributed it to Darwin's concept of sexual selection. Females might quite simply prefer to mate with males with big noses. If so, then males with larger noses will have more females, and therefore more offspring, than males with small noses. In which case, genes for big noses would spread throughout the population. This is much the same concept as why peacocks have large tails — females choose to mate with males which have big, spectacular tails. To us, perhaps, a peacock's tail is a rather more attractive adornment than a proboscis monkey's nose, but there is no accounting for taste, and female proboscis monkeys apparently find long, pendulous noses to be the ultimate in good looks.

Above: Figs. 37 & 38. A nose the size of this one should certainly attract the females. Photos: Joseph Tangah.
Opposite: Figs. 39 & 40. Male proboscis monkeys are twice as large as females, and are among the largest arboreal monkeys in the world. Photos: Rudi Delvaux.

Large Stomachs,
Their Uses and Hazards

Proboscis monkeys have greatly enlarged, cow-like stomachs. These contain a vast array of bacteria which ferment the animal's food. Unlike cows, proboscis monkeys do not chew the cud. Like cows, however, their stomachs have two big advantages. First, the bacteria can break down cellulose, which is the main structural part of leaves. So proboscis monkeys can obtain energy from leaves, whereas cercopithecine monkeys, apes and humans cannot. This goes a long way to explaining why colobine monkeys are so successful in forests. The second advantage of the system is that the bacteria deactivate at least some poisons in the food, allowing the monkeys to eat nasty foods which would kill any normal animals including ourselves.

The system does have its disadvantages too, though. If the colobine monkey eats highly digestible foods such as sweet, sugary fruits, the bacteria ferment them so rapidly that gas and acid build up suddenly in the stomach. This highly uncomfortable sounding condition known as bloat can quickly kill the animal. So proboscis monkeys have to forego tasty, sweet fruits such as figs and rambutans, and stick to bitter, tough ones, most of which are pretty unpalatable to us humans with our simple stomachs.

Fig. 41. The perceived resemblance between proboscis monkeys and Europeans gave rise to one of their common local names: *Orang belanda* or "Dutchman". Photo: Julian Cox/ PhotoAsia, Malaysia. **Fig. 42** (opposite). Juvenile proboscis monkey checking for hazards below. Photo: Juan Carlos Muñoz/PhotoAsia, Malaysia.

The mangrove, peat swamp and riverine forests of Borneo are always lush and green, with a superabundance of leaves in all directions all year round. This is paradise, you would think, for a monkey adapted to eating leaves. Staggeringly, there is so little food in many areas that the monkeys have trouble finding enough to survive.

The reason is that the trees have taken steps to protect themselves against the depredations of hungry animals. Some such as rattans and nibong palms make themselves physically unpleasant, producing huge barrages of long spines and thorns. A more widespread tactic of the trees is to fill their leaves with chemicals which are harmful to animals. Proboscis monkeys and other colobines generally cope with this better than other animals, since their stomach bacteria can deactivate certain poisons. On the other hand, if the plants contain lots of fibre and tannin which impede digestion, the monkeys quite simply cannot break them down before they would starve to death. Moreover, some plants contain chemicals that act as antibiotics. Proboscis monkeys cannot eat these either because they would kill the bacteria in their stomachs; without the bacteria, the monkey could not eat many of its other foods, so it has to nurture the bacteria and avoid eating anything which harms them.

Most of the mature leaves in these coastal swamp forests are extremely tough and fibrous, full of lignins and tannins, which means that they are not available as a food source for the monkeys. Instead, proboscis monkeys have to resort to young leaves, which are less fibrous. But they are also far

scarcer and more scattered in the forest. During the course of a year, about half of the animal's diet is made up of young leaves with just a few mature leaves.

Proboscis monkeys cannot top up their diet with sweet, succulent fruits either, because of the problem of bloat. So the other half of their diet is made up of non-sweet fruits and seeds, such as those of the nutmeg, legume and palm families. These too are often hard to find, especially during certain months of the year when few trees are producing fruits. So all in all, proboscis monkeys are faced with "leaves, leaves everywhere but not a lot to eat".

This diet is typical of colobine monkeys, mixing young leaves, non-sweet fruits and seeds. It is a very different diet to that of a primate with a simple stomach. Orang-utans, gibbons and macaques cannot get energy from young leaves, but they can eat succulent fruits without fear of bloat. So their diet is made up of sweet fruits such as figs and a wide variety of other wild fruits, supplemented by a few tender young leaves and a variety of other items such as termites.

The different digestive systems of the primates means, then, that they cannot eat many of the same foods as each other. Gibbons would poison themselves if they ate many of the legume seeds gorged on by proboscis monkeys, and proboscis monkeys would die from bloat if they had a fig feast. It also explains why, more often than not, if a group of noisy, small macaques crashes through a group of more sedentary proboscis monkeys, the two species largely ignore each other. They are looking for different foods, are not competing, so have no need to interact.

Functions performed by having a complex stomach (proboscis monkeys and other colobines) compared to a simple one (monkeys, apes and humans). + means the stomach type can do that; — means the stomach type cannot do that.

	Complex stomach	Simple stomach
Obtain energy from leaves	+	—
Deactivate poisons	+	—
Make some vitamins	+	—
Re-cycle nitrogen	+	—
Digest sweet, energy-rich fruits	—	+
Digest rich, easily-accessible protein	—	+

Travel — Proboscis Monkeys on the Move

Daily travel patterns of proboscis monkeys are determined by two main factors — the location of good food sources, and rivers. The animals sleep in trees adjacent to rivers every night. After dawn, they usually go into the forest away from the river in search of food, although occasionally they amble through the trees near the river for the whole day. Their food is often scarce and scattered, so these large animals have to travel long distances to get enough of it. In fact, their food is so scarce that proboscis monkeys travel further each day than most other species of forest monkey. On some days they go up to 2 km, whereas most other forest colobines average 800 m or less. The area used by an animal or group of animals during the course of a year is known as the home range. All other rain forest colobines studied to date have a home range less than 1 sq km in size. The distance that proboscis monkeys have to travel to find enough food varies between habitats, but in all

Fig. 43. Adult male displaying at a rival. Photo: Armin Maywald/ PhotoAsia, Malaysia.

Figs. **44** (above), **45** & **46** (opposite). Proboscis monkeys are spectacular leapers, often successfully making jumps that initially appear impossible. Photos: Rudi Delvaux. **Fig. 47** (right). Female carrying her infant across the mangrove mud as the tide is going down. **Fig. 48** (below). Two adult males on mangrove mud at low tide. It is unusual to see two fully-grown males peacefully together. Photos: Ch'ien C. Lee.

of them, their home ranges are larger than other forest-dwelling colobines. At the lower end of the scale, in peat swamp forests in Kalimantan, food is relatively abundant so each group of proboscis monkeys only needs to roam through about 1.4 sq km. In Sukau in Sabah, they roam a little more widely with each group using about 2.2 sq km, whereas in the mixed riverine forest and mangroves of Samunsam in Sarawak, each group uses about 9 sq km during a year. This area is often long and thin since the animals rarely go more than 800 m from a river, so their home range is usually a strip of forest along both sides of the river. In areas with several rivers, the home range is a series of interconnected strips along the different waterways.

The home range of a group of proboscis monkeys often spans different forest types. The animals might, for example, feed on seeds in riverine forest for part of the year, and migrate downriver into mangrove forest to feed on young leaves there when food in the riverine forest is scarce. This is exactly what happens in Samunsam Wildlife Sanctuary in Sarawak, and is why they cover such a lot of ground in the course of a year.

Different groups of proboscis monkeys use exactly the same areas as each other. This is quite unusual, since many animal species exclude others from their home ranges so that they have exclusive access to the food there. But each group of proboscis monkeys either has to travel so far to find food that it cannot possibly defend all that area against others, or else the distribution and abundance of food is such that it just is not worth the energy to try to defend it. In either case, proboscis monkeys do not attempt to do so.

An animal that travels widely in areas riddled with networks of rivers and creeks has to be able to swim, and proboscis monkeys are very good at it. They have partly webbed back feet which help them to swim, and also to

Fig. 49. Juvenile female launching herself across a gap in the canopy. Photo: K. Wothe/PhotoAsia, Malaysia.

walk on mangrove mud without sinking in. They swim using a sort of doggy paddle, moving slowly but with the absolute minimum of noise and splashing. For relatively wide rivers such as the Samunsam River in Sarawak, the animals slide extremely quietly into the water and swim across in single file with no noise or splashing at all. The assumption is that this is to avoid attracting estuarine crocodiles, which are predators of proboscis monkeys; crocodiles are attracted to prey by splashing. By contrast, crossing narrower rivers such as the Menanggol in the Kinabatangan area of Sabah, the proboscis monkeys use an entirely different technique. They climb high into trees by the river's edge, then from about 10 metres up, hurl themselves out and down to land in the river with a colossal splash. This area also has crocodiles, but on the other hand, the river is so much narrower that a single wild leap takes the animal two-thirds of the way across, with only a couple of metres to swim. Maybe a much shorter time in the crocodile's river compensates for making such a commotion.

Apart from crocodiles, the other problem of swimming is faced by infant proboscis monkeys. They travel by clinging to their mother's front. Imagine their surprise when they suddenly find themselves hurtling through the air and are then plunged into water and unable to breathe! After a few seconds underwater, the infant clambers further up its mother's front, so a little face appears over her shoulder as the infant comes up for air.

Scarcity of food explains why proboscis monkeys need to travel large distances and have to cross crocodile-infested rivers. But it does not explain why they sleep right next to a river every single night. It is not because that is where all the food is; often the best feeding trees are a short distance away from the river. So what is it about the river that makes it such a great place to spend the night?

Early observers assumed that proboscis monkeys sleep by the river to avoid predators; that the river

Fig. 50. Proboscis monkeys are highly proficient swimmers, moving quietly through the water using a type of "doggy paddle". Photo: Ch'ien C. Lee.

on one side, and water below, offered protection from the clouded leopard, Borneo's largest cat. Clouded leopards do indeed eat proboscis monkeys, but so too do crocodiles which are probably at least as great a threat. It is not wise to have an escape path from clouded leopards which involves leaping into the potential jaws of crocodiles below. Also, if it is a good way to avoid predators, all of the other primates should sit by the river at night, which they do not. Another possibility is that it is cooler by the river at night. With their large stomachs brewing away, and large body size, proboscis monkeys might try to keep cool at night. Doing so might be easier by a river with its circulating air currents. This was tested by hanging thermometers by the river and inland, but the temperatures were no different. Another theory down the drain!

In which case, why do proboscis monkeys sleep by the river at night? It is probably related to their unusual social lives. Females move between harems. In order to decide whether or not they should move, and where they should go, they need to size up the different males to see which is the strongest, fittest, and likely to father the best children. Riversides are obvious places for the females to have a good look at the males because they are open with good visibility. Not only can the females size up the males, but the good views also mean that riversides are ideal places for males to display and show off their prowess. They also allow males to keep a better eye on their rivals.

So we can now revise our picture and say that a proboscis monkey's travel is influenced by two factors: food and the demands of its somewhat strenuous social life.

Natural Predators of Proboscis Monkeys

The proboscis monkey does not have to face the problem of big predatory cats since none occur in Borneo. There are no tigers or leopards here, and the largest cat is the clouded leopard. Surprisingly, perhaps, since they hunt mainly on the ground and proboscis monkeys live mainly in trees, clouded leopards do sometimes eat proboscis monkeys, and we have the photographic evidence to prove it. We also know of cases where proboscis monkeys have been eaten by reticulated pythons which grow up to almost 10 metres in length, and are clearly very capable of taking proboscis monkeys. Eagles are other potential predators of proboscis monkeys while they are in the trees.

Possibly the greatest natural predators of proboscis monkeys are in the water, notably both species of crocodile that inhabit the rivers and estuaries of Borneo. The estuarine crocodile is a voracious killer of anything that moves in rivers and, within Borneo, estuarine crocodiles and proboscis monkeys generally live in the same sites, mangroves and riverine areas close to the coast. Nobody has ever seen them eating proboscis monkeys, but they kill several people in Borneo every year and are obviously capable of taking large monkeys. Surprisingly since it is known predominantly as a fish-eater, Borneo's other crocodilian, the false gharial, has been seen to take proboscis monkeys. The monkeys are most vulnerable when walking on mangrove mud or swimming across the river, where they have little defence against such formidable predators.

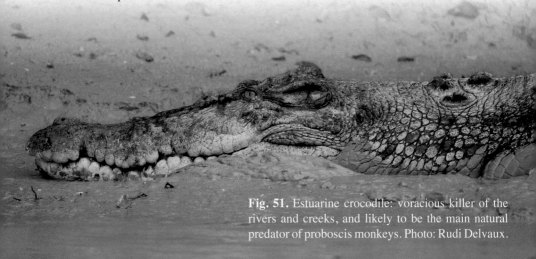

Fig. 51. Estuarine crocodile: voracious killer of the rivers and creeks, and likely to be the main natural predator of proboscis monkeys. Photo: Rudi Delvaux.

Fig. 52. The best time to watch proboscis monkeys is in the early evenings as the different groups gather by the rivers and sort out their social lives. Photo: Paul Swen.

A Day in the Life of a Proboscis Monkey

Proboscis monkeys are active in their swamp and riverine forests during the day, and sleep in trees adjacent to a river at night. In general, they are not such early risers as the other primates there which are up and away almost as soon as dawn has broken. Proboscis monkeys usually wake within half an hour of dawn, but sometimes do not leave their sleeping trees for some two hours more. Most commonly, they move away by an hour after dawn, but it is inclined to be earlier if there are many other groups of proboscis monkeys nearby, and later if it is raining.

On waking in the mornings, the first main event of the day is breakfast. Proboscis monkeys do not usually sleep in a good food tree, so they have to move at least a short distance to eat. They sometimes remain close to the river, swim across it or, as often as not, move a short distance away from it into the forest for their first meal of the day. Then follows a general bout of feeding. Frequently, most of the group sits in one tree. Even so, it is rare to see more than two or three animals at a time due to the denseness of the riverine and mangrove trees; an infant squealing and crashing through the branches in play, the occasional fruits dropping from above and the sight of a few tails from time to time are the only signs to any human below that the animals are there.

After the first main feed of the day, the proboscis monkeys usually (but not invariably) move further from the river. Surprisingly, perhaps, the male is not the leader of the group. The first animal to move off is usually an adult female who then leads the group, while the male is inclined to tag along near to the back.

Fig. 53. The first main activity of the day — breakfast! Photo: Ch'ien C. Lee.

Fig. 54. Juvenile "threatening" a human observer. Photo: Rudi Delvaux.

Fig. 55. "Don't come near my females!"
Photo: Rudi Delvaux.

After food and travel comes a rest. All colobine monkeys have long rests throughout the day, while they digest the leaves or other tough foods they have eaten. Proboscis monkeys, with their unusually large stomachs, carry this to extremes. Once at Samunsam in Sarawak, they had breakfast, moved inland into a tree to rest at 7.50 a.m., then stayed in the same tree for eight hours before moving off for a large meal before dusk. Somewhat tedious for the scientist under the tree! A post-breakfast rest of one to two hours is more common, though, and the animals spend the remainder of the morning and most of the afternoon alternating between feeding, resting and travelling. About two hours before dusk, the monkeys start to move back towards the river and have one more feeding session before darkness falls.

As the proboscis monkeys approach the river, the different groups often come together, and it is now that the animals are most active, especially on nights when there is no rain. From time to time, an adult male displays, so the gentle evening sounds of birds and insects are shattered by roaring and branch crashing. Meanwhile, the females carry on feeding or grooming their infants, and the juveniles play, chasing and wrestling with each other in the beautiful, clear evening light. With several groups assembling by the river, such activity

Fig. 56. This group, heading up the river bank, has a subadult and adult male, together with the females and their young. Photo: Paul Swen.

Fig. 57. The main peak of mating activity is around the middle of the year. Photo: FLPA/Hugh Lansdown/ PhotoAsia, Malaysia.

Fig. 58. Male proboscis monkeys are sometimes unexpectedly left on their own if young animals succeed in interrupting mating. Photo: Ch'ien C. Lee.

is enormously spectacular under the bright orange and pink evening equatorial sky.

Not all evening gatherings comprise such noisy hordes. Sometimes a group potters down to the river on its own and settles with the minimum of noise and fuss.

By dusk, the monkeys have moved up into a suitable sleeping tree and are settling down for the night. Sleeping trees are generally tall and fairly open so visibility is good. This presumably allows the animals to keep an eye out for predators, as well as for males from other groups sneaking in during the night. It possibly also allows them a good overview of where the best place is for breakfast. By the time the nightjars are swooping around and the bats hunting for insects low over the river, the proboscis monkeys are asleep.

Not all days are exactly the same. On some days, the monkeys spend very little time resting and seem to be on the move all day, whereas on others they sleep for most of the time between the post-dawn and pre-dusk feeding bouts. Sometimes they meet other groups, sometimes they do not. In summary, the daily lives of proboscis monkeys, like that of all animals, are determined ultimately by the amount and distribution of food available at the time, together with the need to avoid predators and find good mates.

Fig. 59 (left). Their complex stomachs allow proboscis monkeys to obtain energy from fibrous leaves. **Fig. 60** (right). They often choose young, less fibrous leaves, and can strip whole trees of their young foliage. Photos: Ch'ien C. Lee.

Proboscis Monkeys
in Captivity

Proboscis monkeys do not generally do well in captivity. They are extremely sensitive, appear to get depressed after a few days, stop eating and die. This depression could be because of poor captive diets upsetting their delicate digestive system, or because of stress. In any case, they rarely survive long once taken from the wild.

There are a very few zoos which have kept them for long periods. In spite of several zoos in North America and Europe acquiring proboscis monkeys in the middle of the last century, only the Bronx Zoo in New York managed to keep and bred them successfully for many years, with the last two animals from there eventually being sent to Singapore Zoo in 2003. Keeping the monkeys in Southeast Asian zoos, which allows access to a wide range of their natural foods, is proving in some cases to be more successful.

Unfortunately, proboscis monkeys are such spectacular animals that many zoos want to keep them, whether or not they have the correct facilities and expertise to do so. Since there are so few proboscis monkeys in captivity, the easiest way for zoos to acquire the animals is to take them from the wild. In almost all cases, this would be disastrous for wild populations. Proboscis monkeys live in harems. Taking an adult male away disrupts breeding of an entire social group. In Sarawak at least, the largest single population of proboscis monkeys has only about ten harems, therefore ten breeding males. Removing even one of them would stop breeding and disrupt the social

Fig. 61. Generally, proboscis monkeys do not do well in captivity. They appear depressed, stop eating and soon die. This animal had been caught a week previously and was chained up outside a kampung shophouse. Photo: Elizabeth Bennett.

Fig. 62. Whether in the wild or in captivity, the male's enormous nose does sometimes get in the way. Photo: Vojtech Vlk/PhotoAsia, Malaysia.

life of 10% of the entire population. Moreover, with the very high mortality rate in captivity, at least two animals would probably need to be caught for every one which ends up in a zoo. So the effect on many of the already tiny wild populations would be devastating.

Fortunately, the wildlife authorities in all regions of Borneo are fully aware of the problems and continue to refuse permission to capture proboscis monkeys from the wild in almost all cases.

If the animals for zoos are acquired without threatening a wild population, and with extremely careful management, proboscis monkeys in zoos can be important in conservation education. A professionally planned exhibit with good information and graphics teaches people about the animals, their habitats, and the problems facing them. For many people in towns, their first encounters with wild animals are often zoos. If these are properly designed with education and conservation as their primary aims, they can be important in showing people, many of them for the first time, the splendour of wildlife and value in preserving it.

Another important role that zoos can play for an endangered animal is to breed it. If a species is endangered in the wild, it can be taken into captivity, and bred to establish one or more assurance colonies of the species. That means that we have some insurance and back-up in case the absolutely appalling happens and the species becomes extinct in the wild. The aim would be that, after successful breeding in captivity at some later date, the offspring are introduced back into the wild. This has been done successfully with a few species such as the North American bison, golden lion tamarin, and Arabian oryx. It is far from easy, however, and there are no guarantees. Each different species provides an array of tough and sometimes insurmountable challenges. If the animals are endangered in the wild because their habitat has been destroyed, there might be nowhere left for the captive-bred animals to be released. Another problem is if captive animals are released into a place where there is already a wild population of the same species, because there is a risk that they might have picked up some infections in captivity which they then pass on to the wild population. This could devastate a whole population of an already endangered animal. An alternative is to put the captive-bred animals into areas where there are no wild ones. But that leads to the question of why aren't there wild ones there? Is it because they have been hunted out? In which case, there is no guarantee that the captive-bred animals will not meet the same fate. Or maybe there are no monkeys there because the habitat is not suitable in some way, in which case, released animals would not survive.

With extremely careful research and planning, top captive facilities, and properly planned reintroduction programmes, captive breeding can be a highly useful conservation tool. The ultimate goal of any conservation programme is to save the animals in the wild. All good captive breeding programmes are done in parallel with programmes to conserve the species in the wild. Not only does that ensure their survival there, but also conserves their habitats and the many thousands of animal and plant species with which they live and interact, and also the highly beneficial ecological role that those habitats play in the life of our planet.

Proboscis Monkeys and the Future

In 1964, the American zoologist J.A. Kern said that, due to the inaccessible nature of the proboscis monkey's habitat, and the fact that it was of little economic value, the monkey's future was not threatened. Since then, the picture has changed dramatically, and the proboscis monkey is now threatened throughout its range. There are two main problems: first, disturbance and loss of the habitat, and second, hunting.

Generally, the places where proboscis monkeys occur are those which are most developed and inhabited by humans — flat coastal plains and riversides. Most people live along rivers, most large towns are near rivermouths, and most large-scale agricultural schemes are on the flat coastal plains. Such human pressure is the reason why proboscis monkeys are facing so many problems.

Loss of habitat

The proboscis monkey's main habitats are mangrove, peat swamp and riverine forests. Riverine forests are inevitably in thin strips, and are generally highly disturbed by the presence of towns, villages, agriculture, and by river transport. Few rivers in Borneo remain undisturbed, especially along their lower reaches where the monkeys are generally found.

In mangroves, traditionally wood was cut for firewood and charcoal, but generally such cutting was small scale and presented no great threat to the monkeys. In some areas, however, mangrove forests have been subject to logging so intensive that few trees are left. This has been to obtain poles for use in the local building industry, and wood and woodchips for export. Only a few areas of mangrove remain that have not been heavily cut in this way. Additional areas have been cleared to make prawn ponds for commercial aquaculture.

The proboscis monkey's other main habitat is peat swamp forest. Peat swamps are accessible and full of valuable timber, so they have been heavily

Fig. 63 (opposite). The conservation functions of intact mangroves and the commercial felling of mangrove stands cannot both be maintained without careful planning and knowledge of the dependence of wildlife on mangroves. Photo: Elizabeth Bennett.

logged. If only a few trees are taken out, proboscis monkeys are able to survive. Some areas of peat swamp forest have been heavily and repeatedly logged, however. In the 1970s and 1980s, such logging was sometimes followed by treatment of the forest to try to enhance the next timber crop. Treatment involved poisoning of non-timber trees, many of which were good food trees for the monkeys. This practice has now been discontinued, but was undoubtedly responsible for the deaths of many monkeys, as well as major degradation of some of their peat swamp forests. Forest fires along rivers also can be damaging. The infamous Bornean fires of 1997–1998 were another set-back, and reportedly destroyed more habitat used by proboscis monkeys than that of any other primate.

As lowland forests with ideal conditions for agriculture are increasingly cleared, pressure increases on the more marginal peat swamps and mangroves to be converted to agriculture as well, including to oil palm plantations. This

Fig. 64. The spread of oil palm plantations is destroying proboscis monkey habitats across much of Borneo. Photo: Rudi Delvaux.

is in spite of the enormous ecological importance of maintaining such habitats in their natural state since such coastal wetlands protect the environment in many critical ways. Mangroves are some of the most productive natural areas in the world, and are of enormous value to humans. So their destruction is highly damaging to our interests, as well as destroying the unique wildlife there.

Between these various forms of habitat disturbance, few intact areas of habitat remain within the entire range of the proboscis monkey. Each group of proboscis monkeys travels over large distances to find enough food, so populations need extensive areas of forest to survive. Few patches of forest, and even fewer reserves, are now large enough to include the entire area used by proboscis monkey groups during a year. Even if the monkeys only use food from outside a reserve for one month a year, they will die if the reserve becomes isolated.

Valuable Mangroves

Mangroves are forests which grow between the low and high tide levels, so they are inundated with salty water every time the tide is up. To keep themselves anchored firmly in the mud when the tide swishes around them, many of the trees have great networks of stilt roots above the mud. Apart from the seawater coming in every tide, mangroves are also fed by water coming in from inland rivers. These carry silt laden with nutrients, often from far in the interior of Borneo. As the rivers reach the mangrove, they slow down. The silt settles out and is trapped under the trees by the complex of roots. The nutrients are then taken up by the trees. When their leaves and fruits eventually drop, they are broken down by crabs and fungi to form a huge supply of food for fish, prawns and other sea-dwelling animals, both in the mangrove itself, and also way out to sea where the detritus is carried by the outgoing tide.

A case study conducted in the early 1990s showed that, in the Kuching Division of Sarawak alone, mangroves supported fisheries worth more than RM50 million every year, and provided jobs for some three thousand fishermen. Cutting down mangroves results in the loss of all of that valuable seafood and jobs. Another problem that arises when mangroves are cut is that all of the mud trapped by the tree roots suddenly washes out to sea and is deposited on sandy beaches all along the coast. This mud has been accumulating for hundreds of years. It is black, smelly and makes beaches extremely unpleasant. The same case study showed that, again, in the Kuching Division of Sarawak, that would ruin tourist beaches that brought in a revenue of about RM20 million every year. Thus, mangroves are not only essential for their wildlife; they are highly valuable for humans.

Fig. 65 (above). The inflorescences.
Fig. 66 (below). The propagule on a leafy twig.
Fig. 67 (opposite). The habit of *Rhizophora stylosa*.

Photos: Ubaldus M.

Hunting

In some of the few remaining areas of reasonably undisturbed forest, proboscis monkeys are hunted. It is unclear how much hunting was a problem in the past, especially in interior areas near major rivers. But increasingly, indications are that it might have been significant in some areas, potentially accounting for the limited and patchy distribution of the species along many major rivers.

In coastal areas, traditionally, hunting was not a major problem because the people living in and around the proboscis monkey's habitats are predominantly Moslems, who do not eat monkeys. With the advent of speedboats and shotguns, however, people have increasingly been going into mangrove areas from nearby towns and hunting for sport. The proboscis monkeys' habit of sleeping conspicuously next to rivers every evening makes them especially vulnerable to hunters in boats, and large numbers can be killed in a short time. The number of proboscis monkeys in one hunted area in Sarawak dropped by 50% in five years.

Current status

The result of habitat loss and hunting means that number of proboscis monkeys is becoming alarmingly low in some areas. In Sarawak, there are probably one thousand animals or less in the whole State. These are divided into several small, isolated populations, none of which is totally secure. In Brunei Darussalam, the proboscis monkeys live in the mangroves of Brunei Bay, where they cross between Brunei Darussalam and Sarawak. They are hunted on the Sarawak side of the border, which reduces their population. There are probably 200 or less remaining. In Sabah, numbers are higher because of the large populations in the Kinabatangan River and Dent Peninsula areas, and recent estimates point to perhaps 6000 animals occurring in the State. In Kalimantan, the species is undoubtedly more abundant because of the large areas of swamp forest and stricter control of firearms, and some individual populations are up to about 1000 animals. But no comprehensive recent surveys have been done. The population in the Mahakam Delta, which would have numbered in the thousands until the early 1990s, has now been decimated due to conversion of the coastal swamps to shrimp farms, and the species is now extinct in Pulau Kaget Nature Reserve where it was once abundant.

Many of the proboscis monkey populations now are extremely small and far from others. Small, isolated populations of any animal suffer from inbreeding, and are also vulnerable to occasional disasters such as major storms or disease. Thus, many of the small populations will slowly die away. This is already happening in western Sabah and parts of Sarawak.

Conservation measures

Proboscis monkeys are protected by law in all regions of Borneo. This means that it is illegal to hunt or keep them or their parts, and penalties for doing so are high. Under international trade regulations (CITES, the Convention on International Trade in Endangered Species of Wild Fauna and Flora) the proboscis monkey is listed on Appendix I. This means that it is illegal to move it between countries for commercial purposes. Export and import permits are needed, and should only be given if the animal is being moved for scientific or conservation reasons. Thus, on paper at least, the animal is well protected against being hunted, kept as a pet or traded. It is often difficult to enforce the law in areas riddled with waterways, however, especially when the wildlife authorities are extremely short of staff in all regions.

All regions of Borneo have systems of totally protected areas (TPAs) for protecting their wildlife and forests. Almost all of Borneo's large reserves are in the interior, however, not in areas where proboscis monkeys occur. The

Fig. 68. Another main habitat type, peat swamp forest, is also subject to legal and illegal logging. Here, logs are collected prior to removal by railway line. Photo: Elizabeth Bennett.

only exception is Danau Sentarum National Park in Kalimantan where the proboscis monkeys occur in large inland swamps. Coastal reserves throughout Borneo are mostly too small to protect proboscis monkeys effectively; the monkeys are so wide-ranging, they need large areas to survive. The only TPAs in the coastal plains large enough to protect the monkeys effectively are Tanjung Puting National Park in Kalimantan, and possibly Lower Kinabatangan Wildlife Sanctuary in Sabah and Maludam National Park in Sarawak; the remainder are either too small, or in habitat that is marginal so the numbers of monkeys are small.

Support for conservation of proboscis monkeys is increasing, however, especially since they are increasingly a major draw for tourists. Awareness of the ecological importance of protecting coastal swamp forests and riverbanks is also on the rise, and a flurry of admittedly small protected areas in the coastal plains of Sarawak and Sabah have been protected in recent years. If such trends continue, and can be complemented by vigorous anti-hunting measures in all areas, the hope is that these unique and spectacular animals will survive in the wild for future generations to enjoy.

Fig. 69. Conversion of forests to oil palm plantations involves clearance of all natural vegetation and, with that, loss of all habitat for proboscis monkeys and countless other species of animals and plants. Photo: Paul Swen.

Seeing Proboscis Monkeys in Borneo

S ome of the places where proboscis monkeys occur are not open to the public, and others are remote and inaccessible. So this is not giving a total list of where proboscis monkeys occur, but a sample of the most accessible places where you can easily go and the chances of seeing the monkeys are high.

In all of these places, bear in mind that proboscis monkeys are most active in the early morning just after dawn, and in the two hours or so before dusk. These are also the times when the animals are alongside rivers, so plan your trips so that you are in the proboscis monkey areas at those times. With careful planning, and a little bit of luck, you will have a wildlife experience that you will always remember.

Fig. 70. With their habit of coming to riversides each evening, proboscis monkeys provide a unique and unforgettable experience for tourists in boats. Photo: Arthur Chung.

MALAYSIA: SABAH

Lower Kinabatangan

The lower Kinabatangan region of Sabah is the best place in northern Borneo for spectacular views of large numbers of proboscis monkeys. The highest density of the animals in the area is in the vicinity of Kampung Sukau. The area has much other dramatic wildlife, including Bornean pygmy elephants, Bornean orang-utans, Bornean gibbons, red langurs, silvered langurs, long-tailed and pig-tailed macaques, bearded pigs, deer, hornbills, eagles, kingfishers — a wealth of some of Borneo's most impressive animals. Some such as proboscis monkeys and hornbills you can see from the river; to see others, you have to go into the forest on foot.

There are several ways of getting there, the easiest of which are:
1. Take a boat from behind the fish market in Sandakan to Suan Lamba. There are daily scheduled morning services, or else you can charter your own boat. At Suan Lamba, local minibuses and taxis take you by road to Kampung Sukau. At Sukau, charter a local boat to take you along the rivers.
2. Take a minibus from Sandakan, near the Community Centre, to Sukau. At Sukau, charter a local boat to take you along the rivers.
3. Charter a boat from Sandakan, across Sandakan Bay and down to Kampung Abai or Sukau. This is easy but much more expensive than the previous two options.
4. Take a bus from Sandakan to the Kinabatangan bridge. (The bus ultimately goes to Lahad Datu.) At the bridge is Kampung Batu Puteh where you charter a local boat to take you along the river.
5. By far the easiest option is to take a tour through a local travel agent, many of which offer transportation to and within the area and overnight accommodation.

Klias River

This is a good option if you are in Kota Kinabalu (KK) and not heading to the east coast. Different operators offer tours from KK, leaving KK by bus/minibus in the early afternoon, and travelling for approx 2.5 hrs to Klias Wetlands. You then take a boat trip starting around 4 pm. In addition to good

Fig. 71. Serene mood of the mighty Kinabatangan — home to the proboscis monkeys. Photo: Rudi Delvaux.

Fig. 72. A group of proboscis monkeys at the feeding station, Labuk Bay Sanctuary, Sabah. Photo: J. & C. Sohns/PhotoAsia, Malaysia.

Fig. 73. Visitors at Labuk Bay Sanctuary, Sabah. Photo: Joseph Tangah.

sightings of proboscis monkeys, as it gets dark you get wonderful views of flashing fireflies. Most tours include dinner after the boat trip before heading back to KK, arriving there around 9 pm.

Labuk Bay Proboscis Monkey Sanctuary

This privately-operated centre in a mangrove area near Sandakan has a feeding station with excellent views of proboscis monkeys. Although some visitors prefer a less artificial setting, it is ideal for close-up photography. Access from Sandakan is from Jalan Labuk towards KK, turn off at the SPS 3 junction at Mile 19 adjacent to Consolidated Sabah Farms. From here, the sanctuary is 15 km in along the road. The sanctuary also provides transport, day trips, and overnight stays. Some local tour operators also arrange trips there.

MALAYSIA: SARAWAK

Bako National Park

This small park is close to Kuching, and proboscis monkeys can readily be seen by walking quietly along the mangrove plankwalks or some of the other trails leading out from the park headquarters. Take the trails from the headquarters at Telok Assam to either Telok Paku or Telok Delima soon after dawn or before dusk and you stand a good chance of seeing the animals, especially on the wooden plankwalk near the start of the trail to Telok Paku. Other animals which you should easily see are long-tailed macaques, silvered langurs and bearded pigs. The Park is also famous for its different coastal forest types, large numbers of pitcher plants, spectacular rock formations, sunsets and lovely beaches. To get to the park, drive, or take a bus from Kuching to Kampung (= village) Bako. From there to the park is by boat, and there are always charter boats waiting at the Kampung Bako jetty, for a fixed price (about RM40 per boat each way at the time of going to print). You can either take a day trip or, to stand the best chance of seeing the animals round dawn and dusk, stay overnight. A variety of hostels and rest houses is available at cheap prices. Booking is through the National Parks booking office, Visitor Information Centre, 1 Jalan Tun Haji Openg, Kuching (next to the newer building of the main Sarawak Museum). Telephone no.: (082) 248088.

Kuching Wetlands National Park

This is also close to Kuching, and in recent years has become a great place for seeing mangrove and other coastal wildlife, including proboscis monkeys and also Irrawaddy dolphins, as well as mudskippers, fiddler crabs, and coastal birds. Boat-based wildlife tours depart from Santubong, either the village or boat club depending on which tour operator. Most tours head to the Salak and Santubong river estuaries for dolphin watching then head up the Salak River to watch proboscis monkeys. Most sightings occur at Salak Island and in the mangroves just opposite Salak Island within the national park where the chances of seeing proboscis monkeys are extremely high. Sunrises, sunsets and rainbows here with the mountains of Santubong and Serapi as backdrops are often spectacular.

BRUNEI DARUSSALAM

Bandar Sri Begawan

Most tour operators in Bandar Sri Begawan offer boat tours to see proboscis monkeys in the mangroves close to the city. Trips last 3–4 hours, with morning or afternoon departures. Other mangrove wildlife and scenery and spectacular sunsets again are attractions.

INDONESIA: KALIMANTAN

Danau Sentarum National Park, West Kalimantan

This large park protects a highly diverse inland lake system with a large population of proboscis monkeys, as well as a wide diversity of other wildlife including orang-utans, Storm's storks, possibly three species of crocodilians, and a wide diversity of fish. About 700 km upriver from the coastal regional capital of Pontianak, access is by flight from Pontianak to Putussibau then upriver for about 7 hrs by longboat. Some local accommodation is available, and some local tour operators arrange trips. The park office is in Jln. Abdurahman Saleh 33, Pontianak. Telephone/fax: +62-561-734613.

Kutai National Park, East Kalimantan

Go by road from Samarinda to Boman. The National Parks office there provides permits and assistance with boat hire. Take a small boat to the mangroves around Teluk Kaba. This can be done as a day trip, or else you can stay overnight at the Park Headquarters at Teluk Kaba. Generally, there are good views of proboscis monkeys in the mangroves. Rehabilitant orang-utans at Teluk Kaba are an additional attraction.

Tanjung Puting National Park

Fly from Jakarta, Semarang, or Pontianak to Pangkalanbun; each has daily flights. Obtain a permit for the park in Pangkalanbun. Go by road to Kumai and obtain your permit from the Park Headquarters there. Charter a boat to Tanjung Puting. This is a regular tourist route and is easy to do. It is possible to stay at the hotel at Tanjung Harapon. If you keep the small boat with you, you can spend several days exploring the Sikonyer Kanan river although, at the time of going to print, it would be advisable to avoid the Sikonyer Kiri river due to illegal gold mining there. Apart from large numbers of readily visible proboscis monkeys in the Sikonyer Kanan river area, additional attractions are rehabilitant orang-utans and a wide range of other peat swamp and lowland forest wildlife.

Acknowledgements

It was way back in 1984 that I first went to Sarawak to study proboscis monkeys. That was the beginning of 18 years living and working in the State, first on the conservation of proboscis monkeys and their wetland habitats, subsequently moving onto a range of other projects, including with some work in Sabah. During that time, very many people both in Sarawak and Sabah, and also in my parent organization in New York, the Wildlife Conservation Society (WCS) have supported my work, and me personally — too many to name here, but their contributions are all greatly appreciated.

The home of the work on proboscis monkeys was the Sarawak Forest Department and I am especially grateful to its then-director, Datuk Leo Chai, and also to the successive heads of the National Parks and Wildlife Office: Paul Chai, Philip Ngau Jalong, Ngui Siew Kong and Sapuan Haji Ahmad, as well as to the then Head of Wildlife Management and Research, Francis Gombek. The work on proboscis monkeys was funded by WCS and WWF Malaysia. The Royal Malaysian Air Force was very generous in providing aerial support on many occasions. I would like to thank Anthony Sebastian, Rajanathan Rajaratnam and Ramesh Boonratana ("Zimbo") for their wonderful collaborations in the field, and for allowing me to include again here their information and ideas on proboscis monkeys. The proboscis monkey fieldwork could not have been done without the support of Dato' Dr Mikaail Kavanagh, Lady Y.P. McNeice, Ken Scriven, Thomas Struhsaker, Archie (Chuck) Carr III, Mary Pearl, Martha Schwartz and the staff of Samunsam Wildlife Sanctuary. I also appreciate the long-term friendship and support in Sarawak of Ann Armstrong, Cynthia Chin, Melvin Gumal, Jayl Langub, Gill Raja, Isai Raja, and Philip Yong. WCS's continual support for nearly 30 years from the proboscis monkey studies to the present time is deeply appreciated and many people in WCS have been wonderful over the years; special thanks to John Robinson. Many thanks also to Datuk C.L. Chan for inviting me initially to write and subsequently to revise the book, and for being so positive, cheerful and helpful at all times, to Noviar Andayani, Melvin Gumal and Wayne Tarman for digging out the latest information on seeing proboscis monkeys in the wild, and to Karen Phillipps and Ken Searle for, once again, providing a wonderful working environment for writing the revised version of this book.

Suggested Further Reading

If you have enjoyed this book and would like to find out more about Borneo's wildlife or about other primates, the following books might be of interest.

Campbell, E.J.F. (2011). *A Walk through the Lowland Rain Forest of Sabah*. Natural History Publications (Borneo), Kota Kinabalu in association with Borneo Rainforest Lodge, Lahat Datu.

Cubitt, G. and Payne, J. (1990). *Wild Malaysia*. New Holland, London in association with the World Wide Fund for Nature, Kuala Lumpur.

Cubitt, G., Whitten, T. and Whitten, J. (1992). *Wild Indonesia*. New Holland, London.

Davison, G.W.H. (1992). *Birds of Mount Kinabalu, Borneo*. Natural History Publications (Borneo), Kota Kinabalu and KOKTAS Berhad, Ranau.

Hazebroek, H.P. and Abang Kashim bin Abang Morshidi (2000). *National Parks of Sarawak*. Natural History Publications (Borneo), Kota Kinabalu.

Hazebroek, H.P., Tengku Zainal Adlin and Waidi Sinun (2004). *Maliau Basin: Sabah's Lost World*. Natural History Publications (Borneo), Kota Kinabalu.

Hazebroek, H.P., Tengku Zainal Adlin and Waidi Sinun (2012). *Danum Valley: The Rain Forest*. Natural History Publications (Borneo), Kota Kinabalu.

Hutton, Wendy (2004). *Sabah Colour Guide: Kinabatangan*. Natural History Publications (Borneo), Kota Kinabalu. [with photographs by Cede Prudente]

MacKinnon, J.R. (1974). *In Search of the Red Ape*. Collins, London and New York.

MacKinnon, K., Hatta, G., Halim, H. and Mangalik, A. (1996). *The Ecology of Kalimantan, Indonesian Borneo*. Periplus Editions, Singapore.

Payne, J., Francis, C.M. and Phillipps, K. (1985). *A Field Guide to the Mammals of Borneo*. The Sabah Society, Kota Kinabalu and WWF Malaysia, Kuala Lumpur.

Phillipps, A., Lamb, A. and Lee, C.C. (2008). *Pitcher Plants of Borneo*. Second Edition. Natural History Publications (Borneo), Kota Kinabalu.

Phillipps, Q. and Phillipps, K. (2011). *Phillipps' Field Guide to the Birds of Borneo*. Second Edition. Beaufoy Books, Oxford.

Rowe, N. (1996). *The Pictorial Guide to the Living Primates*. Pogonias Press, New York.

Sha, J.C.M., Matsuda, I. and Bernard, H. (2011). *The Natural History of the Proboscis Monkey*. Natural History Publications (Borneo), Kota Kinabalu.

Scientific Names of Animals and Plants

ANIMALS

Arabian oryx	*Oryx leucoryx*
Baboons	*Papio* spp.
Banded langur	*Presbytis melalophos*
Bats	Chiroptera
Bearded pig	*Sus barbatus*
Bornean gibbon	*Hylobates muelleri*
Bornean orang-utan	*Pongo pygmaeus*
Chimpanzees	*Pan* spp.
Clouded leopard	*Neofelis diardi*
Colobus monkeys	*Colobus* and *Procolobus* spp.
Common chimpanzee	*Pan troglodytes*
Common langur	*Semnopithecus entellus*
Deer	Cervidae
Douc	*Pygathrix* spp.
Eagles and kites	Accipitridae
Elephant	Elephantidae
Bornean pygmy elephant	*Elephas maximus borneensis*
Estuarine crocodile	*Crocodylus porosus*
European bison	*Bison bonasus*
False gharial	*Thomistoma schlegelii*
Gibbons	Hylobatidae
Golden lion tamarin	*Leontopithecus rosalia*
Golden monkeys	*Rhinopithecus* spp.
Gorilla	*Gorilla* spp.
Hornbills	Bucerotidae
Kingfishers	Alcedinae
Leopard	*Panthera pardus*
Long-tailed macaque	*Macaca fascicularis*
Macaques	*Macaca* spp.
Nightjars	*Caprimulgus* and *Eurostopodus* spp.
Orang-utan	*Pongo* spp.

Pig-tailed macaque	*Macaca nemestrina*
Pygmy chimpanzee	*Pan paniscus*
Proboscis monkey	*Nasalis larvatus*
Red langur	*Presbytis rubicunda*
Reticulated python	*Python reticulatus*
Silvered langur	*Trachypithecus cristatus*
Simakobu	*Simias concolor*
Tiger	*Panthera tigris*

PLANTS

Figs	*Ficus* spp.
Legumes	Leguminosae or Fabaceae
Nibong palms	*Oncosperma horridum*
Nipa palm	*Nypa fruticans*
Nutmegs	Myristicaceae
Palms	Palmae
Pitcher plants	*Nepenthes* spp.
Rambutans	*Nephelium* spp.

Photo: Marc Ancrenaz.

Glossary of Terms Used

All-male group: Social group comprising males of different ages. Very occasionally, one or two females may temporarily join it. No breeding occurs in the group. It has a loose social structure, with animals joining and leaving it frequently.

Alluvial: Pertaining to the silt and soil deposited by rivers along their floodplains and deltas. This soil is rich in minerals and other nutrients, and plants growing there are generally highly productive.

Ape: Primate belonging to the super-family Hominoidea but excluding humans. Apes are characterised by having relatively very large brains and no tails. The lesser apes comprise the Asian gibbons. The greater apes are the common and pygmy chimpanzees and gorillas of Africa and orang-utans of Asia.

Bacteria: Microscopic one-celled plants. Many cause diseases, but some can be beneficial, e.g., those that ferment milk to yeast, and those in the stomachs of certain specialised animals (cows, goats, colobine monkeys) which help to digest the food.

Cercopithecine: Monkey belonging to the sub-family Cercopithecinae. They are found throughout Asia and Africa, and there are about 70 species. They are generalised monkeys with simple stomachs. They live in forests but, unlike colobines, some species also thrive in more open and man-made habitats.

Colobine: Monkey belonging to the sub-family Colobinae. They are found throughout Africa and Asia, there are about 50 species. They are all characterised by having complex stomachs containing bacteria which ferment the food. Apart from the common langurs of India, they are restricted almost entirely to forests.

Complex stomach: Stomach comprising a greatly expanded first section containing bacteria to ferment the animal's food, and a smaller, acidic lower chamber. The main advantages of the stomach are allowing the animal to digest cellulose (the main structural component of leaves) and to eat foods containing certain poisons without being harmed.

Genes: The basic unit of inheritance. The nucleus of every cell in an organism contains many thousands of genes which, between them, programme all aspects of the animal's form, functioning and certain aspects of its behaviour.

Grooming: Cleaning of the body surface by licking, nibbling, scratching or picking with the fingers. In primates, this has both hygienic and social functions.

Gunung (Malay): Mountain.

Habitat: The area and particular type of area in which an animal or plant lives in the wild.

Harem: A social group comprising one adult male, more than one adult female and their mutual offspring.

Home range: The area used by an animal or group of animals during a year.

Kampung (Malay): Village.

Macaque: Monkey belonging to the genus *Macaca*. There are about 21 species of macaque, all but one of which only occur in Asia. They are generally brown, lively monkeys in large social groups. They live in both forests and more open areas. They are intelligent opportunists with an eclectic diet, so many species thrive in agricultural and other human-influenced areas.

Mammal: Animal of the order Mammalia. Females of all mammal species produce milk to succour their young. Most mammals have four limbs and are covered with hair.

Mangrove forest: Coastal forest growing between the low and high tide levels. Since the trees establish in soft mud and are flooded with salt water every tide, they have developed many specialities such as stilt and aerial roots and the ability to secrete salt.

Nocturnal: Active at night.

Peat swamp forest: Forest growing on deep peaty soils. The substrate is permanently waterlogged and very low in nutrients since the only incoming water is from rainfall.

Prehensile tail: Tail which can cling onto branches and even support the animal's weight.

Primate: Mammals belonging to the order Primates, and comprising prosimians, monkeys, apes and humans. No one feature characterises primates, but they tend to have relatively large brains, agile hands and feet with nails, and good vision with stereoscopic sight.

Prosimian: Primate belonging to the sub-order Prosimii. Prosimians are generally regarded as the most primitive primates. They tend to be small and nocturnal, the only exceptions being the lemurs of Madagascar. Other prosimians include pottos and bushbabies in Africa, and lorises and tarsiers in Asia.

Pulau (Malay): Island.

Riverine forest: Forest growing adjacent to or near a river, generally on productive alluvial soils. In the tropics, it is characterised by being extremely dense and productive, and having large numbers of climbing plants.

Sexual selection: The process whereby certain feature(s) of an animal are preferentially chosen by a member of the opposite sex when choosing a mate. Thus, those features are passed on to future generations. With the passing of generations, if such features continue to be selected, they become exaggerated, such as the tail of a male peacock and nose of a male proboscis monkey.

Simple stomach: Stomach comprising only one chamber which is acidic and in which food is digested by enzymes produced by the animal itself. Such a stomach does not allow the animal to digest leaves or deactivate poisons, but it does allow it to eat a much wider range of other foods than an animal with a complex stomach.

Stereoscopic sight: Sight in which two eyes are facing forward so receive slightly different views of the same image. This gives an impression of depth, and allows the animal to judge distances accurately.

Stilt roots: Roots which emerge from the trunk some distance above the ground and grow down into the soil. They give a tree a very firm foothold if the substrate is loose (e.g., mangrove mud). They might also trap silt in incoming water, which provides extra nutrients to the tree.

Tanjung (Malay): Peninsula.

Tannin: Astringent chemical produced by plants. It slows down digestion in animals eating the plant, so might protect the plant from being eaten too intensively. It occurs differentially in the plant, e.g., is generally in high levels in unripe fruits but much lower levels in ripe ones.

Totally protected area (TPA): Area in which any form of disturbance (e.g., timber extraction, land clearance in any form, building, hunting) is strictly prohibited.

Photo: Rudi Delvaux.

Index

The Author

Elizabeth (Liz) Bennett is the Vice President for Species Conservation at the Wildlife Conservation Society (WCS). Born in the UK, she went to Nottingham University to read zoology, and then to Cambridge University where she gained her PhD for research on the ecology of colobine monkeys in Peninsular Malaysia. She moved to Sarawak, Malaysia in 1984, and lived and worked there for the next 18 years. She started there by conducting the first ever detailed field study of the proboscis monkey. This was followed by state-wide wildlife surveys, and studies of the effects  of hunting and logging on wildlife. Her time in Sarawak culminated in her coordinating a team of Sarawak Government and WCS staff to write a comprehensive wildlife policy for the State, and subsequently to head a unit within the Government to coordinate its implementation. After that, Liz became Director of the Hunting and Wildlife Trade Program at WCS, focusing primarily on bushmeat policies in Central Africa and wildlife trade in China. Her current role involves coordinating WCS's species conservation programs in more than 60 countries across the globe and in WCS's zoos in New York. Liz has published widely, with more than 120 scientific and popular publications, including co-editing a book which is a comprehensive review of the issue of hunting in tropical forests, and co-authoring the World Bank policy paper on the same topic. Her services to conservation have been recognized by her being awarded the "Golden Ark" award by Prince Bernhard of the Netherlands in 1994, the "Pegawai Bintang Sarawak" (PBS) by the Sarawak State Government in 2003, "Member of the Most Excellent Order of the British Empire" (MBE) by Her Majesty Queen Elizabeth II in 2005, and D.Sc. (*honoris causa*) by Nottingham University in 2008.